YOU ARE
TOO MUCH,

CHARLIE BROWN

Selected Cartoons From

BUT WE LOVE YOU, CHARLIE BROWN
Vol. II

by Charles M. Schulz

A FAWCETT CREST BOOK
FAWCETT PUBLICATIONS, INC., GREENWICH, CONN.
MEMBER OF AMERICAN BOOK PUBLISHERS COUNCIL, INC.

YOU ARE TOO MUCH, CHARLIE BROWN

This book, prepared especially for Fawcett Publications, Inc.
comprises the second half of BUT WE LOVE YOU, CHARLIE
BROWN, and is reprinted by arrangement with Holt, Rinehart
and Winston, Inc.

Seventh Fawcett Crest printing, July 1967

Published by Fawcett World Library,
67 West 44th Street, New York, N. Y. 10036
Printed in the United States of America

SOME PEOPLE DON'T LIKE TO HAVE THEIR FAULTS POINTED OUT..

SCHULZ

ONLY TEN MORE SHOPPING DAYS UNTIL BEETHOVEN'S BIRTHDAY

SHOPPING DAYS?!

SCHULZ

PRIDE OF OWNERSHIP...

SCHULZ

SAY, THIS SOUNDS LIKE A GOOD DEAL..

IF YOU BUY A USED CAR AT THIS PLACE, YOU GET ALL SEVEN BEETHOVEN CONCERTOS FREE! ISN'T THAT A GOOD DEAL?

UH HUH

I LIKE TO SEE GOOD MUSIC MADE AVAILABLE TO THE AVERAGE MAN..

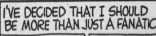
I'VE DECIDED THAT I SHOULD BE MORE THAN JUST A FANATIC..

I'M GOING TO BE A **WILD-EYED** FANATIC!!

THROW ONE...
GET BACK
FIVE...

ALWAYS GIVE THE
CLIENT MORE THAN
HE ASKS FOR!

WELL, I JUST LEARNED SOMETHING, CHARLIE BROWN..

NEVER JUMP INTO A PILE OF LEAVES HOLDING A WET SUCKER!

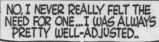

BAAHHHHH!!

SCHULZ

DEAR PENCIL-PAL, HOW DO YOU GO TO SCHOOL? I RIDE IN A SCHOOL BUS.

I GO TO A BIG SCHOOL. WE LEARN A LOT IN OUR SCHOOL.

THEY TEACH US SCIENCE, ENGLISH, GEOGRAPHY, ARITHMETIC, HISTORY AND SPELLING.

WHEN I GET BIG I WOULD LIKE TO DRIVE A SCHOOL BUS.

SCHULZ

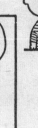